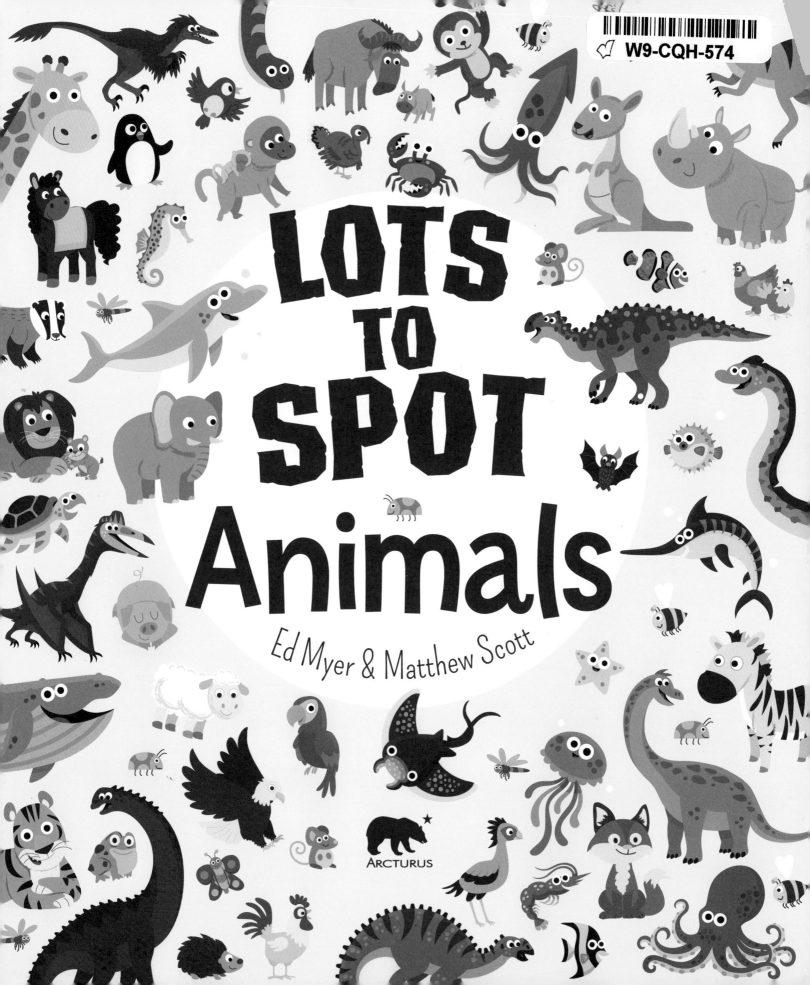

LOTS TO SPOT

Animals

Ed Myer & Matthew Scott

ARCTURUS

ARCTURUS

This edition published in 2019 by Arcturus Publishing Limited
26/27 Bickels Yard, 151–153 Bermondsey Street,
London SE1 3HA

Edited by Susannah Bailey
Written by William Potter
Illustrated by Ed Myer and Matthew Scott
Designed by Trudi Webb

ISBN: 978-1-78950-112-4
CH006976NT
Supplier 29, Date 0119 Print run 7916

Printed in China

CONTENTS

225 million years ago, the first dinosaurs appeared. The Earth was very hot, with no ice at the North and South Poles.

Find 5

Mastodonsaurus
(MAS-toe-don-sore-us)
This huge, frog-like creature was the largest known amphibian.

Find 5

Tanystropheus
(tan-ee-STROFE-ee-us)
Tanystropheus was a long-necked reptile that could dip its head into water to catch fish.

Find 5

Liliensternus
(lil-ee-en-STERN-us)
The largest land predator of its day, it had a jaw full of sharp teeth.

Find 5

Plateosaurus
(PLAT-ee-o-sore-us)
This dinosaur could stand on its back legs to reach tree leaves.

Find 3

Gerrothorax
(jeh-row-THORE-ax)
Gerrothorax was a flat creature, like a giant tadpole, which lived in and out of water.

Find 5

Placochelys
(plack-oh-KELL-iss)
Placochelys was one of the earliest known turtles, with a flat, knobbly shell.

Find 5

Saltopus
(SALT-o-puss)
This meat-eating dino walked on two legs and was the size of a cat.

Find 2

Ruehleia
(roo-LAY-ah)
An early sauropod, Ruehleia had a small head and a long neck and tail.

Find 6 Thecodontosaurus
(THEE-co-DON-toh-sore-us)
A skinny, plant-eating dino, it hid in caves when threatened.

Find 5 Procompsognathus
(pro-comp-SOG-nay-thus)
This small, fast hunter would have eaten insects and lizards.

5

GRAZING GIANTS

The late Jurassic was a time of giant, long-necked sauropods that ate from the tallest trees.

Find 3

Brachiosaurus
(BRACK-ee-uh-sore us)
This dino was so large, an adult human could only reach its knee.

Find 3

Hesperosaurus
(hes-PARE-uh-sore-us)
A plant-eater with round plates on its back, Hesperosaurus used its tail to defend itself.

Find 3

Apatosaurus
(ah-PAT-uh-sore-us)
Like all sauropods, Apatosaurus ate plants, such as conifers and ferns.

Find 5

Dryosaurus
(DRY-o-sore-us)
This ostrich-sized dino lived on leaves. Its name means "tree lizard."

Find 3

Allosaurus
(AL-oh-sore-us)
Allosaurus was the biggest meat-eater in North America.

Find 3

Camarasaurus
(kuh-MARE-uh-sore-us)
A sauropod with a shorter neck than others, it ate plants near the ground.

Find 3

Gargoyleosaurus
(gar-GOYL-ee-oh-sore-us)
This dinosaur's spiky back protected it from attack.

Find 3

Stegosaurus
(STEG-uh-SORE-us)
Stegosaurus had diamond-shaped plates along its back and a spiked tail.

Find 3

Diplodocus
(di-plo-DO-kus)
Although Dippy was one of the longest land animals, it had one of the smallest brains.

Find 4

Camptosaurus
(CAMP-tuh-sore-us)
This plant-eating dinosaur walked on two legs.

150 million years ago, large reptiles called pterosaurs ruled the skies, along with the first birds.

Find 6

Gnathosaurus
(NATH-oh-sore-us)
This pterosaur had a spoon-shaped beak and teeth as sharp as needles.

Find 6

Pterodactylus
(ter-oh-DAK-til-us)
Pterodactylus had wings made of skin stretched between its arms and legs.

Find 5

Anurognathus
(an-YOOR-og-NATH-us)
Anurognathus, a small, flying creature, fed on insects such as damselflies.

Find 1

Dakosaurus
(DACK-oh-sore-us)
Dakosaurus, a huge, toothy sea monster, was related to the crocodile.

Find 6

Aerodactylus
(AIR-oh-DAK-til-us)
This duck-sized pterosaur was named after a Pokémon character.

Scaphognathus
(sca-fog-NAYTH-us)
Scaphognathus had
a long tail and
a bony crest
on its head.

Find 6

Find 5

Rhamphorhynchus
(RAM-for-INK-us)
This pterosaur
scooped up fish
with its curved
beak full of teeth.

Find 8

Dimorphodon
(di-MORF-oh-don)
Dimorphodon was
a large-headed
pterosaur that
hunted small prey,
including insects.

Find 9

Libellulium
(li-bel-LUL-ium)
The prehistoric dragonfly,
Libellulium, was as big as a sparrow.

Find 4

Archaeopteryx
(ar-kee-OP-ter-ix)
This early bird was the size of a
pigeon, and had claws on its wings.

It's 75 million years ago and a hungry Albertosaurus is on the hunt.
Run for your life!

Find 5

Pachyrhinosaurus
(PAK-ee-rye-no-SORE-us)
This elephant-sized dinosaur had a horned plate protecting its head.

Find 4

Centrosaurus
(SEN-tro-sore-us)
Centrosaurus was a horned, plant-eating dinosaur that lived in a large herd.

Find 8

Corythosaurus
(ko-RITH-uh-sore-us)
These dinos called to each other with loud, trumpet-like noises.

Find 6

Atrociraptor
(a-TRO-see-rap-tor)
This small raptor would be only a snack for Albertosaurus!

Find 5

Prosaurolophus
(pro-SORE-rol-uh-fus)
The plant-eating Prosaurolophus had a mouth like a duck's bill.

Edmontonia
(ed-mon-TOE-nia)
This plant-eater was built like a tank, with spikes all over its back.

Find 5

Pachycephalosaurus
(pak-ee-SEF-ul-lo-sore-us)
Pachycephalosaurus had a domed, spiky skull it could use for head-butting.

Find 7

Lambeosaurus
(LAM-be-uh-sore-us)
A giant plant-eater, Lambeosaurus had two head crests and pebbly skin.

Find 5

Find 1

Albertosaurus
(al-BERT-oh-sore-us)
This fast predator hunted eight million years before T. rex.

Find 3

Euoplocephalus
(you-op-luh-SEF-uh-lus)
These dinos had hammer-like, clubbed tails they could swing.

Find 4

Eotyrannus
(ee-oh-ti-RAN-us)
Eotyrannus, a small raptor, was an early relative of T. rex.

Find 3

Hylaeosaurus
(HIGH-lee-oh-sore-us)
Hylaeosaurus, a plant-eater, was one of the first dinosaurs to be discovered.

Find 3

Pelorosaurus
(pel-oh-ROW-sore-us)
This long-necked sauropod ate tough plants with its super-strong teeth.

Find 3

⌐LOODLAND FⱢAST
125 million years ago, the sea levels rose and forests around the coasts became flooded.

Baryonyx
(bare-ee-ON-ix)
These dinos might have used their long claws to spear fish.

Find 7

Hypsilophodon
(hip-sih-LO-fuh-don)
Hypsilophodon, a fast plant-eater, was the size of a large dog.

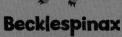

Find 3

Becklespinax
(beck-el-SPIEN-ax)
This meat-eating
dinosaur would
have hunted
Pelorosaurus.

Find 5

Iguanodon
(ig-WAN-oh-don)
The fern-eating
Iguanodon was one
of the first
dinosaurs to be
given a name.

Find 5

Neovenator
(nee-oh-ve-NAY-tor)
A small and fast
raptor, it was
a threat
to Iguanodon.

Find 4

Polacanthus
(pol-a-KAN-thus)
This plant-eating dinosaur
had rows of spikes along its back.

Find 8

Valdosaurus
(VAL-doe-sore-us)
The name of this small
dinosaur means "forest lizard."

Find 5

Hybodus
(HY-bo-dus)
A prehistoric fish that looked like a great white shark, but was much smaller.

Find 4

Xiphactinus
(zee-FACT-in-us)
Xiphactinus, a large, fanged fish, was a strong swimmer that hunted smaller fish.

Find 8

Ichthyosaur
(ICK-thi-o-sore)
This predator looked like a dolphin with large eyes and a jaw full of sharp teeth.

Find 3

SAVAGE SEAS
The prehistoric oceans were home to large reptiles who were just as dangerous as the dinosaurs on land.

Elasmosaurus
(ee-LAZ-mo-sore-us)
A fish-hunting reptile, it had a neck as long as its body!

Find 5

Kronosaurus
(CROW-no-sore-us)
Kronosaurus was the size of a small whale and a dangerous predator.

Archelon
(ar-KEL-on)
Archelon was one of the largest turtles to have ever lived.

Find 7

Protosphyraena
(pro-toss-fy-RAY-na)
This swordfish-like creature had lots of razor-sharp teeth.

Find 9

Mosasaurus
(MOSS-a-sore-us)
The largest of the underwater predators, this lizard was the "T. rex of the seas."

Find 3

Nautilus
(NOR-til-us)
Nautilus, a shelled, tentacled creature, is still found in today's oceans.

Find 5

Ammonite (AM-on-ite)
This squid-like creature grew from thumb size to the size of a tractor wheel.

Find 10

Champsosaurus
(CHAMP-soh-sore-us)
Champsosaurus was a reptile that caught fish in its long, narrow jaws.

Find 8

Find 13

Thescelosaurus
(THES-kel-oh-sore-us)
This plant-eating dinosaur was about as tall as a cow.

Find 4

Albertosaurus
(al-BERT-oh-sore-us)
Albertosaurus, a fierce predator, could run very fast on its strong back legs.

SWAMP DWELLERS

Welcome to the swamp! Many different kinds of dinosaurs hunted and grazed here, alongside other prehistoric creatures.

Find 5

Adocus
(ah-DOH-kus)
This ancient reptile looked a lot like today's turtles.

Find 3

Puertasaurus
(PWUHR-tah-sore-us)
Puertasaurus was as long as three double-decker buses!

Find 4

Triceratops
(try-SEH-rah-tops)
Triceratops used its huge horns to fight off fierce predators!

Find 8

Pteranodon
(tuh-RAN-oh-don)
Pteranodon, a flying reptile, had a crest on its head.

Find 5

Edmontosaurus
(ED-mon-toe-sore-us)
This duck-billed dinosaur lived in large groups and ate plants.

Find 3

Ankylosaurus
(AN-kih-loh-sore-us)
A plant-eating dinosaur that had a club at the end of its tail.

Find 7

Anzu (AN-zoo)
Anzu was a bird-like dinosaur, with feathers, claws, and a beak!

17

T. REX TUSSLE

It's a battle of the giants, as T. rex and Gorgosaurus fight it out to be king of the Cretaceous period!

Find 1

Tyrannosaurus rex
(tye-RAN-uh-sore-us)
One of the largest meat-eating monsters on land, T. rex could crush bone in its jaws!

Find 4

Ornithomimus
(or-nith-uh-MY-mus)
Ornithomimus was a fast-running, clever dinosaur that looked very like an ostrich.

Find 5

Dryptosaurus
(DRIP-tuh-sore-us)
This predator had a claw on each hand as long as a kitchen knife.

Find 7

Thescelosaurus
(theh-SEL-uh-sore-us)
A short, bird-like dinosaur, Thescelosaurus could have eaten both plants and animals.

Find 2

Alamosaurus
(AL-uh-mo-sore-us)
This dinosaur giant was a gentle plant-eater, not a fighter.

18

Find 1

Gorgosaurus
(GOR-go-sore-us)
Though not as large as T. rex, Gorgosaurus had a bite that was just as nasty!

Find 5

Leptoceratops
(lep-toe-SAIR-uh-tops)
Leptoceratops, a human-sized dinosaur, could chew on the toughest plants.

Find 5

Ojoraptorsaurus
(oj-joe-RAP-tuh-sore-us)
Ojoraptorsaurus was a raptor that looked like a large bird, with feathers and a small beak.

Find 5

Dracorex
(DRAK-o-rex)
This dino was named by Harry Potter fans as "Dracorex Hogwartsia."

Find 6

Saurolophus
(sawr-OL-o-fus)
This duck-billed dino had a bony spike on the back of its head.

Baby dinosaurs were born from eggs. The parents sometimes protected their nests from hungry visitors.

Find 2

Troodon
(TRO-uh-don)
Troodon was a goose-like dinosaur that sat on and guarded a nest of up to 24 eggs.

Find 9

Troodon young
(TRO-uh-don)
Hatchlings had tiny feathers, just like their parents.

Find 4

Parasaurolophus
(par-ah-sore-OL-uh-fus)
The crest on this dino's head was a long, hollow tube.

Find 5

Dragonflies
Prehistoric dragonflies were much bigger than today's insects.

Find 3

Edmontosaurus
(ed-MON-tuh-sore-us)
This plant-eating dinosaur had about 1,000 diamond-shaped teeth.

Find 3

Panoplosaurus
(pan-OP-lur-sore-us)
Panoplosaurus was protected by a tough back and spikes on its shoulders.

Find 6

Brachychamsa
(brack-ee-CHAM-sa)
This early alligator lurked in the water, eyeing the hatchlings hungrily.

Find 6

Hadrosaurus
(HAD-ruh-sore-us)
Hadrosaurus dug hollows in the ground to make nests.

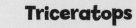

Find 3

Triceratops
(try-SAIR-uh-tops)
A bulky dinosaur that weighed the same as two African elephants.

Find 4

Helopanoplia
(hell-o-pan-OP-li-a)
This early turtle lived mostly in the water.

A pack of small Velociraptors would hunt as a team to catch much larger prey.

Find 10

Velociraptor
(veh-loss-ih-RAP-tor)
Packs of these feathered raptors chased, surrounded, and trapped lone dinos.

Find 6

Gallimimus
(gal-uh-MY-mus)
One of the biggest of the bird-like dinosaurs, Gallimimus was as tall as a giraffe.

Find 5

Harpymimus
(HAHR-pee-MY-mus)
Harpymimus only had a few bottom teeth, used for grabbing food.

Find 4

Protoceratops
(pro-toe-SAIR-uh-tops)
This plant-eater had a beak-like jaw and front claws for digging.

Find 5

Altirhinus
(al-tuh-HIN-us)
A large plant-eater that had an odd, arched bone on its snout.

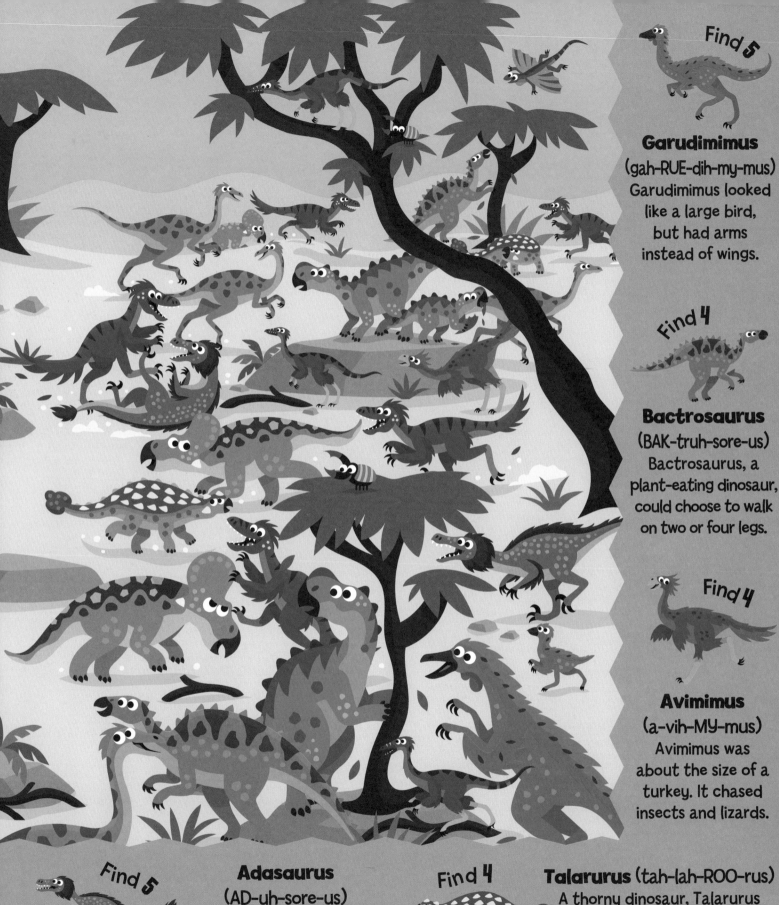

Garudimimus
Find 5

(gah-RUE-dih-my-mus)
Garudimimus looked like a large bird, but had arms instead of wings.

Bactrosaurus
Find 4

(BAK-truh-sore-us)
Bactrosaurus, a plant-eating dinosaur, could choose to walk on two or four legs.

Avimimus
Find 4

(a-vih-MY-mus)
Avimimus was about the size of a turkey. It chased insects and lizards.

Find 5
Adasaurus
(AD-uh-sore-us)
This part-feathered dino had raised, hooked claws on its back feet.

Find 4
Talarurus (tah-lah-ROO-rus)
A thorny dinosaur, Talarurus had rows of spikes from its neck to its tail.

BUSY BARN

The horses share their barn with other animals that like the comfort of a dry, straw bed.

Find 4

Horses

Every morning each horse is groomed and taken for a ride in the fields.

Find 3

Ponies

Ponies are small horses with thicker manes and coats.

Find 3

Donkeys

Donkeys are related to horses. They are smaller, but very strong.

Find 2

Llamas

The woolly llama is a camel relative from South America that only eats plants.

Find 2

Find 4

Barn owls and owlets

Owls often nest in old buildings. Their babies have soft, downy feathers.

Swallows
These fast-flying birds catch insects in the air to feed to their hungry young.

Find **7**

Chickens
The chickens explore the cosy barn for beetles and other insects.

Find **7**

Mice
The mice sneak into the barn to nibble on grain and the other animals' feed.

Find **3**

Saddles
Putting on a saddle makes riding a horse more comfortable.

Find **3**

Rats
The brown rat will eat almost anything. Birds must guard their eggs.

Find 7

Ducks
Ducks need to keep their feathers clean to make them waterproof.

Find 4

Moorhens
This water bird has long toes to help it walk over lily pads and mud.

Find 6

Frogs
Frogs catch insects with their sticky tongues.

POND SPLASHING
The pond is home to farm ducks and geese, as well as some wild visitors!

Find 5

Dragonflies
A dragonfly is born underwater, as a tiny bug called a nymph.

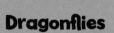

Find 2

Nests
The moorhens and coots build nests from grass and twigs.

Find **2**

Toads
Toads are larger than frogs and have more warts.

Find **5**

Coots
Coots do not like other water birds near their nests.

Find **6**

Geese
Geese eat mostly grass and make lots of honking noises.

Find **1**

Grey heron
This tall bird stands very still, waiting to catch a fish or frog.

Find **13**

Tadpoles
Tadpoles are young frogs that have left their eggs (which are called frogspawn).

In early summer it's time to shear the sheep, so the shepherd leads her flock down from the hills.

Find 1

Shepherd
The shepherd carries a stick called a crook to help guide the sheep.

Find 2

Sheepdogs
Sheepdogs are trained to follow the shepherd's commands and herd the sheep.

Find 11

Ewes
Female sheep are called ewes. Some breeds have horns.

Find 4

Black sheep
Some sheep are born with black fleeces.

Find 3

Feeding troughs
As well as grass, ewes are given extra feed to help them produce milk.

Find 3

Rams
Rams are adult male sheep. They have longer horns than the females.

Find 5

Rabbits
The sheep share the fields with wild rabbits that also eat the grass.

Find 4

Young ewes
The younger female sheep have not grown their horns yet.

Find 8

Crows
Crows use wool from the sheep to help line their nests.

Find 9

Lambs
Playful lambs love leaping and running around in the fields.

BEST IN SHOW

At the country show, local farmers show off their best animals in competitions.

Find 4

Prize cups
The owner of the best animal in each competition wins a cup.

Find 8

Horses
The horses take part in competitions, and pull visitors along in carts.

Find 11

Rosettes
Different rosettes are awarded for first, second, and third prize.

Find 4

Tractors
Some of the tractors on display are very old!

Find 5

Bulls
The bulls are judged on their health, size, and strength.

Pigs
Many handsome breeds of pig are on display, all cleaned and brushed.

Find 6

Sheep
The sheep have had their fleeces trimmed so they look their best.

Find 7

Foals
In a show-jumping competition, these foals jump over a series of fences.

Find 4

Carriages
Horses pull carriages and smartly-dressed visitors around the showground.

Find 4

Horseboxes
Horses are brought to the show in horseboxes, pulled by cars.

MACHINES IN ACTION

These vehicles and machines are used for planting and harvesting crops on the farm.

Find 10

Tractors
A tractor is slow, but it can pull heavy machinery across a muddy field.

Find 3

Spreaders
These spread fertilizer over a field to help crops grow.

Find 3

Four-wheel drive cars
Farmers need a vehicle they can drive over roads and rough tracks.

Find 2

Seed drills
These plant seeds in tidy rows in the fields.

Find 6

Cats
Farm cats are very useful for catching mice.

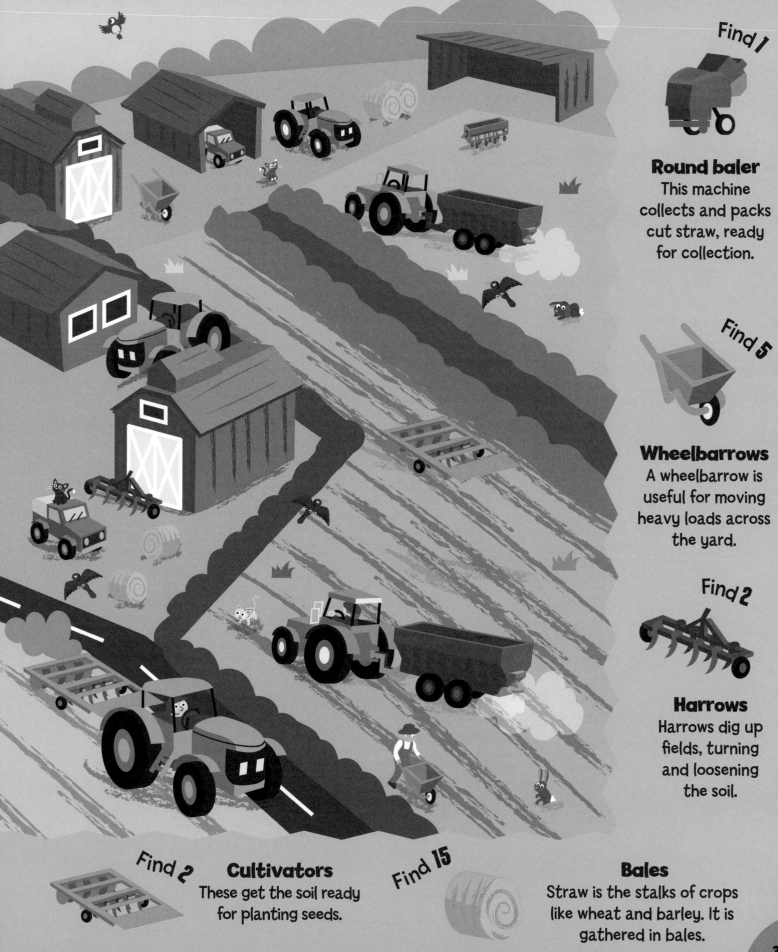

Find 1

Round baler
This machine collects and packs cut straw, ready for collection.

Find 5

Wheelbarrows
A wheelbarrow is useful for moving heavy loads across the yard.

Find 2

Harrows
Harrows dig up fields, turning and loosening the soil.

Find 2

Cultivators
These get the soil ready for planting seeds.

Find 15

Bales
Straw is the stalks of crops like wheat and barley. It is gathered in bales.

COSY FARMHOUSE

In the farmhouse kitchen, there are many things that started out in the farm fields.

Find 7

Fried eggs
Eggs come from hens, ducks, and geese. Then they're cooked in the kitchen.

Find 8

Sausages
Sausages are normally made from pork or beef.

Find 7

Cheeses
Most cheese is made using milk taken from cows.

Find 1

Butter
Butter is made from the fat in cow's cream or milk.

Find 5

Bottles of milk
A cow's milk is usually collected twice a day.

Find 11

Pears
These pears were picked from trees in the orchard.

Find 2

Slices of bread
Bread is made using flour, which is formed by grinding crops like wheat or rye.

Find 9

Fruit preserves
These are made from fruit heated up with sugar. Delicious!

Find 1

Sweater
The wool for this piece of clothing came from sheep.

Find 9

Vegetables
Many of these vegetables were planted as crops in the fields.

URBAN FARM

For children living in the city, an urban farm is a great way to get close to animals.

Find 7

Guinea pigs
A guinea pig eats mostly dried grass called hay.

Find 10

Rabbits
The rabbits like company and space to hop about.

Find 6

Goats
Goats will eat almost anything, so keep your snacks out of reach!

Find 6

Piglets
Some piglets have escaped from their pen. Can you spot where they've got to?

Find 6

Lambs
The lambs drink milk from their mother, or from bottles.

Milk bottles
It's not just the farm animals drinking milk!

Ice creams
This ice cream is made from cows' milk.

Chickens
The urban farm has many breeds of chicken.

Find 7

Piles of straw
Straw provides a comfy, dry bed for the animals.

Find 7

Ducks
Some wild ducks visit the farm and eat the chickens' food.

FLYING FRIENDS

The free-range farm looks after lots of birds, and not just chickens!

Find 1

Rooster
The male chicken wakes up the farm with a "cock-a-doodle-doo!"

Find 10

Turkeys
Turkeys like treats, such as apples, plums, and sweetcorn.

Find 5

Quails
A quail is half the size of a chicken and lays tiny eggs.

Find 10

Eggs
Eggs are collected twice each day.

Find 6

Guinea fowls
If these birds see a stranger or a fox, they will make lots of noise!

Find 1

Hen
The hen lays its eggs on a nest of wood shavings in a coop.

Find 9

Sparrows
These wild birds help themselves to the chickens' grain.

Find 4

Poultry feeders
These metal feeders keep the birds' food dry if it rains.

Find 1

Fox
The birds are kept behind fences, away from the fox.

Find 6

Chicken food
The chickens are fed a mix of pellets and cracked corn.

ROUNDUP!

On this ranch, it's time for the cattle to get their regular health checks. But first they need to be rounded up!

Find 3

Windmills
Windmills are used to pump water from underground.

Find 17

Cattle
The cows spend most of the year grazing in open fields.

Find 9

Calves
New calves in the herd need to be counted.

Find 10

Cowgirls and cowboys
All the herders are expert horseriders with amazing rope skills.

Find 7

Lassos
Cow herders throw this loop of rope to catch cattle by the horns.

Find 8

Horses
A horse is the best way to travel over the wild lands where the cattle graze.

Find 10

Cowboy hats
Cowboys wear a wide-brimmed hat to keep the sun off their faces and necks.

Find 4

Coyotes
Small wolves called coyotes are kept away by the herders.

Find 2

Ranch houses
Ranch houses are normally on one level, rather than having stairs.

Find 4

Rattlesnakes
Watch where you step! This snake has a venomous bite!

41

::BABY ANIMAL::

Young animals on the farm need special attention in their first few months.

Find 7

Ducklings
The mother duck tries to lead her ducklings to water.

Find 3

Piglets
Pigs have litters of about 10 piglets twice a year.

Find 3

Kittens
Baby cats drink their mother's milk and play fight with each other.

Find 4

Goslings
Young geese are called goslings. They have little, fluffy feathers.

Find 3

Lambs
Sheep can only feed two lambs. If a third is born, the farmer may need to care for it.

Find 3

Kids
A baby goat is called a kid. It feeds on a nanny goat's milk.

Find 15

Chicks
Newly-hatched hen chicks are kept warm in pens before being set free to roam.

Find 5

Cygnets
Baby swans often sit under their mothers' wings to keep warm.

Find 6

Calves
A young cow stays with its mother for eight months after it is born.

Find 3

Foals
A baby horse can be up and walking just minutes after being born.

OVER THE REEF

In the sunlit shallows of the reef, thousands of fish make their homes among the coral and plants.

Find 5

Clownfish
Clownfish live among the anemones, but don't feel their stings.

Find 8

Angelfish
Stripy angelfish have tiny mouths that they use to feed on sponges.

Find 9

Sweetlips
Sweetlips are thick-lipped, spotty fish, which swim in large groups called schools.

Find 4

Picasso triggerfish
This bad-tempered fish will chase divers away from its nests.

Find 8

Bird wrasses
Wrasses have long snouts for rooting out tiny shrimp and crabs.

Find 6

Butterflyfish
Yellow butterfly-fish will usually stay in pairs for life.

Find 3

Napoleon wrasses
This bump-headed wrasse can grow to human size. It sleeps in a cave at night.

Find 3

Masked pufferfish
The pufferfish uses the coral as its bed to sleep on at night.

Find 4

Parrotfish
Parrotfish have strong teeth for nibbling coral.

Find 7

Soldierfish
These big-eyed, night-time feeders spend the days hiding in the shadows.

45

CHILLY NORTH

At the North Pole, animals make their homes on and under the ice in the freezing-cold Arctic waters.

Find 2

Polar bears
Polar bears hunt seals from the ice, but they are also strong swimmers.

Find 11

Arctic chars
When it is time for it to breed, the char's belly turns red.

Find 6

Ribbon seals
Black-and-white ribbon seals have a thick layer of blubber to keep them warm.

Find 8

Narwhals
This unusual whale has a long tooth that grows like a horn on its head.

Find 4

Beluga whales
These whales are also called "sea canaries" for the twittering sound they make.

Find 4

Walruses
Walruses have two long teeth that help them get out of the water, onto the ice.

Find 9

Arctic cod
The Arctic cod has a type of antifreeze in its blood to help it survive the cold.

Find 5

Guillemots
Guillemots dive underwater for several minutes to catch fish.

Find 1

Bowhead whale
This Arctic whale can smash its way through thick ice to breathe.

Find 7

Ringed seals
This is the smallest and also the most common seal in the Arctic.

DARK DEPTHS

The fish that live in the deepest part of the ocean have special ways to find food in the darkness.

Find 3

Anglerfish
Anglerfish use glowing lures on their heads, like fishing rods, to attract food.

Find 3

Pelican eels
Deep-sea pelican eels use their huge mouths like nets to scoop up meals.

Find 4

Deep-sea jellyfish
The jellyfish in the dark depths put on bright light shows.

Find 3

Hagfish
This slimy, eel-like fish can tie itself into a knot.

Find 1

Giant oarfish
The giant oarfish is six times as long as a human adult.

48

Find 5

Black swallowers

With expanding stomachs, these fish can swallow other, much larger fish.

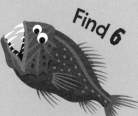

Find 6

Fangtooth

These small fish have long, sharp fangs, used for gripping food.

Find 3

Vampire squid

The vampire squid isn't a bloodsucker, but it has a dark cloak between its tentacles.

Find 4

Viperfish

These sharp-toothed fish can flash lights in their bodies on and off.

Find 11

Lanternfish

Lanternfish have special organs in their bodies that light up.

ROCKY SHORE

The tide washes in and out from the rocky shore twice a day, revealing crabs and shellfish on the sand and stones.

Find 3

Sea stars
If a sea star loses an arm, it can grow it back.

Find 2

Hermit crabs
These small crabs live in shells left behind by other creatures.

Find 4

Common octopuses
The octopus can break open shells with its eight strong arms.

Find 6

Cormorants
Cormorants dry their wings in the sun after diving for fish.

Find 3

Sea scorpions
This camouflaged predator can be mistaken for a rock.

Find 9

Mussels
Mussels live between two shells and glue themselves to rocks using their feet.

Find 3

Common seals
Fish-hunting common seals spend most of their time ashore.

Find 6

Moon jellyfish
This common jellyfish has a bell shape with tiny tentacles around the edge.

Find 6

Common blennies
Blennies can survive out of the water for a short time.

Find 9

Sea urchins
Don't touch! This slow-moving creature grows a shell with sharp spines.

ANCIENT SHIPWRECK

A sunken ship is rusting on the sea bed. It is now a home for corals and fish, and a great place for divers to explore.

Find 6

Lionfish
Beware this stripy fish's spines— they are very poisonous!

Find 8

Redcoat squirrelfish
This fish has a spiky fin along its back and large eyes for finding food at night.

Find 6

Scuba divers
Divers breathe air from a tank so they can swim deep under water.

Find 7

Spadefish
These fish have big, flat bodies. They often swim in large schools.

Find 12

Bluestripe snappers
Bright bluestripe snappers like to swim around corals in groups.

Find 3

Moray eels
Moray eels are snakelike fish with many tiny teeth. They like to hide in the rocks.

Find 4

Devil scorpionfish
This poisonous fish hides in the sand and shuffles along on two side fins.

Find 9

Bannerfish
The bannerfish was named after the long fin on its back.

Find 6

Bluefin trevallies
These strong swimmers will chase and catch much smaller fish.

Find 5

Coral groupers
This big, spotty fish feeds on crab, octopus, and squid.

Kelp is a large seaweed. It may grow to form an underwater forest where sea creatures can nest and graze.

Find 4

Mako sharks
The fastest of the sharks, the mako can reach up to 90kph (56mph).

Find 3

John dory
The john dory has long fins and a large spot on its side.

Find 6

Marblefish
Camouflaged marblefish keep the seaweed trim by nibbling it.

Find 2

Stingrays
Stingrays have spines on their tails that can give you a deadly sting.

Find 4

Red pigfish
Male pigfish grow almost twice as big as the females.

54

Porcupine fish
When in danger, this fish can puff itself up like a spiky balloon.

Find 3

Common triplefins
This tiny fish was named for the three fins on its back.

Find 6

Blue maomaos
Bright blue maomaos swim in large groups near the surface.

Find 7

Yellowtail kingfish
This fast-swimming fish is a prized catch for fishermen.

Find 3

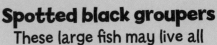

Spotted black groupers
These large fish may live all of their lives in the same part of a reef.

55

Find 2

MANGROVE MAZE

Mangroves are trees that can grow in salty water by the coast. Their underwater roots are a shelter and nursery for young fish.

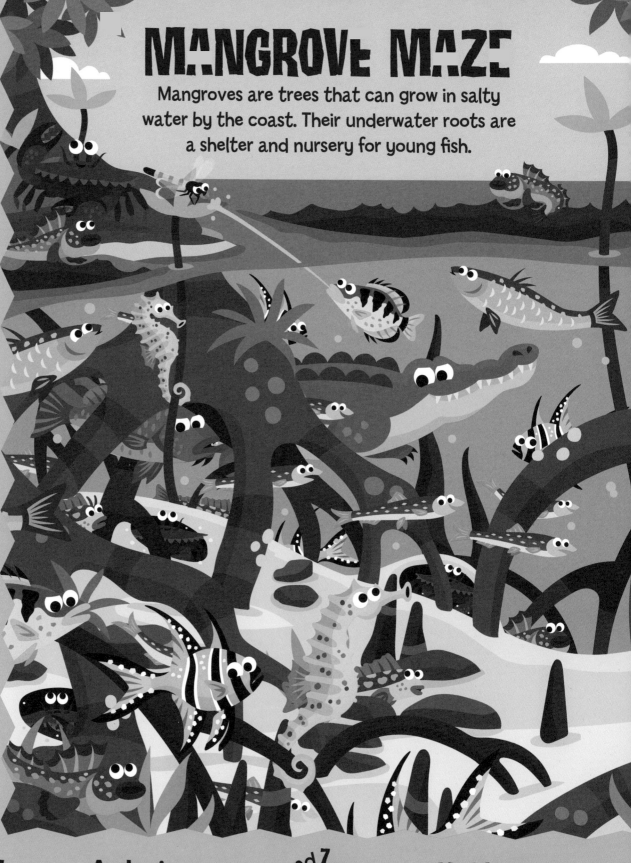

Saltwater crocodiles
The largest reptile on earth will eat almost anything that comes close—including people!

Find 5

Yellow sea horses
Sea horses grip on to the mangrove roots with their tails.

Find 8

Mud crabs
When the water level is low, this crab moves into a burrow or muddy hole.

Find 17

Anchovies
Anchovies are small fish that are often hunted by larger fish.

Find 7

Mudskippers
This fish can survive out of the water, where it uses its fins to flop about.

Banded archerfish
Archerfish will spit at insects to knock them into the water.

Find 4

Mangrove jacks
This hunter will hide in the mangrove roots to surprise passing fish and crabs.

Find 7

Cardinalfish
The male keeps his young safe by carrying them in his mouth.

Find 8

Mullets
Mullets swim near the water's surface, picking at tiny pieces of food.

Find 6

Combtooth blennies
This small, shy fish has two long fins, like combs, on its back.

SUNKEN CITY

Long ago, this city was flooded by the ocean. Its ruins and ancient treasures are now a habitat for plants and fish.

Find 14

Zebra sea breams
The stripy sea bream feeds on small shellfish, worms, and urchins.

Find 5

White-spotted octopuses
When disturbed, this octopus turns a bright red.

Find 7

Dogfish
The dogfish is a type of shark. It has rough skin, like sandpaper.

Find 5

Cornetfish
This long, pipe-like fish can detect prey using its sensitive tail.

Find 4

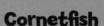

Eagle rays
The ray has a flat body, with large fins and a mouth on its underside.

Find 8

Bearded fireworms
This centipede-like creature can give a nasty sting through its bristles.

Find 4

Red sea stars
These distinctive starfish are bright scarlet!

Find 3

Sea hares
The sea hare is a large underwater slug that feeds on seaweed.

Find 3

Stargazers
This fish buries itself in the sandy sea bed, ready to lunge at small prey.

Find 5

Sea potatoes
This is not a vegetable—it's a spiny urchin that burrows into the sandy bed.

Night time is when many fish choose to hunt.
Soft corals appear and tiny creatures leave their hideouts.

Find 10

Cleaner shrimp
Banded shrimp use their claws to remove bugs from passing fish.

Find 3

Decorator crabs
This crab sticks objects to bristles on its back to camouflage itself.

Find 4

Sea kraits
These highly venomous snakes hunt under rocks for eels and small fish.

Find 15

Polyps
Polyps are tiny animals that connect together to form coral reefs.

Find 5

Epaulette sharks
This small, spotty, crab-eating shark is harmless to humans.

Find 5

Cuttlefish
Cuttlefish are brainy relatives of squid that signal by changing their skin tones.

Find 3

Crown-of-thorns starfish
This huge, poisonous sea star eats coral and destroys reefs.

Find 2

Slipper lobsters
Slipper lobsters have flat feelers on their heads, like plates.

Find 6

Blackspotted puffers
To defend itself, the puffer can swell up with water.

Find 2

Pineapple sea cucumbers
This sea star relative can squirt out its own guts if attacked!

The North Atlantic ocean is home to many fish. Flatfish rest on the sea bed or burrow into the sand. Their skin patterns help them to hide.

Find 8

Clams
These shelled creatures can live for hundreds of years.

Find 4

Lobsters
The American lobster can weigh as much as a five-year-old child.

Find 5

Skates
These flatfish spend most of their time buried in the sand.

Find 4

Horseshoe crabs
This living fossil is more closely related to a spider than a crab.

Find 12

Haddocks
A female haddock can produce up to three million eggs in a year.

Flounders
This flatfish has both eyes on one side of its body.

Find 6

Scallops
Scallops open and close their shells to swim through the water.

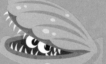

Find 3

Red gurnards
This bottom-dwelling fish has fins that open out like wings.

Find 3

Oyster toadfish
Toadfish use camouflage to catch other fish by surprise.

Find 15

Herrings
The herring is one of the world's most common fish.

63

SUPER SAFARI

The Serengeti of East Africa is a land of grass and trees where large herds of animals graze.

Find 14

African elephants
This is the world's largest land animal. Each elephant herd is led by the oldest female.

Find 9

Lions
The lion lives in a group called a pride. Lions hunt their prey as a team.

Find 12

Wildebeest
Over a million wildebeest roam the Serengeti, seeking fresh grass and water.

Find 5

Cheetahs
The fastest land animal, the cheetah, can sprint at up to 100 kph (60 mph).

Find 12

Baboons
Baboons live in large social groups, often grooming each other.

Find **9**

Impalas
If this noisy antelope spots a lion, it will leap high and dash away.

Find **5**

Black rhinos
This seriously endangered animal has two horns and very thick skin.

Find **11**

Giraffes
The long-necked giraffe can eat leaves out of the reach of other animals.

Find **5**

Crocodiles
The toothy crocodile has been around since the time of the dinosaurs.

Find **12**

Zebras
Zebras follow the wildebeest and eat the dry grass that the wildebeest leave behind.

In the chilly north, many animals have thick, white coats to keep them warm and to help hide them in the snow.

Find 9

Muskoxen
Muskoxen form a circle around their young to protect them from wolves.

Find 8

Arctic hares
The pale, winter fur of the Arctic hare helps it to hide in the snow.

Find 8

Wolves
This ancestor of the pet dog hunts in a pack.

Find 8

Arctic foxes
In summer, Arctic foxes swap their thick, white coats for thinner, darker ones.

Find 9

Reindeer
Reindeer may travel thousands of miles a year in search of food.

Find 3

Snowy owls
With no trees here, owls make nests in hollows on the ground.

Find 11

Snow geese
The snow goose flies south to Mexico in the coldest months.

Find 6

Lemmings
Lemmings dig tunnels to find moss and herbs under the snow.

Find 4

Polar bears
These huge predators stalk seals and walruses from the shore and sea ice.

Find 3

Walruses
Walrus tusks on males can grow as long as human arms.

67

Lynx
The lynx is twice the size of a pet cat with tufty ears and a very short tail.

Find 3

Find 7

Snowshoe hares
These hares have furry pads to stop their feet freezing in snow.

Find 4

Wolverines
Wolverines have jaws strong enough to crush bone.

PINE FOREST
The cool pines in North America keep their leaves all year round, giving shelter to animals big and small.

Find 7

Black bears
The black bear leaves her cubs up a tree while she looks for food.

Find 6

Beavers
Beavers live in waterside lodges made out of mud and sticks.

Find 6

White-tailed deer

These deer raise their white tails as a warning of danger.

Find 5

Moose

The world's largest deer grows new antlers every year.

Find 4

Pine martens

These tree-climbing weasels hunt voles, mice, and birds.

Find 7

Muskrats

This large rodent leaves a strong smell to mark its home.

Find 4

Porcupines

Porcupines are spiny animals that climb trees for berries and nuts.

69

GRASSLAND GRAZERS

The North American prairies are huge areas of grassland with few trees. Summers are dry and winters are very cold here.

Find 9

Bison
There were once 50 million bison roaming the American grassy plains.

Find 5

Golden eagles
Keen-eyed eagles can spot their prey from 2 km (1.2 miles) away.

Find 4

Black-footed ferrets
This rare ferret will chase prairie dogs into their burrows.

Find 9

Burrowing owls
These small owls lay their eggs in underground nests.

Find 10

Jackrabbits
Jackrabbits' long ears have been compared to donkeys' ears.

Find 4

Rattlesnakes
This venomous snake uses a rattle in its tail as a warning to keep away.

Find 4

Coyotes
These small wolves howl loudly at night to announce themselves to rival packs.

Find 7

Pronghorns
At just two days old, the speedy pronghorn can outrun a horse.

Find 4

American badgers
American badgers dig for prairie dogs and mice.

Find 10

Prairie dogs
Prairie dogs keep watch on mounds to guard their underground homes.

The volcanic Galapagos islands, in the middle of the Pacific Ocean, are home to some unique animals.

Find 5

Green sea turtles
Smaller than the tortoises, these turtles spend most of their time diving for seagrass.

Find 11

Marine iguanas
This is the only lizard that finds food in the sea.

Find 6

Flightless cormorants
These native diving birds have lost their ability to fly.

Find 5

Frigate birds
The male frigate bird inflates its red throat sac to attract females.

Find 3

Humpback whales
Humpbacks make a splash by leaping out of the water.

Find 11

Lava lizards
Eye-catching lava lizards bob up and down to claim territory.

Find 4

Giant tortoises
Giant tortoises can live to be 150 years old.

Find 7

Sea lions
These playful sea lions like company and often do tricks in the water.

Find 6

Blue-footed boobies
This bright-footed bird dives from a great height to catch fish in the sea.

Find 4

Fur seals
Fur seals spend most of their time out of the water.

AMAZON ACTIVITIES

The steamy, wet, tropical rain forest contains the largest mix of wildlife and plants in the world.

Find 4

Sloths
Sloths hang from branches and move very slowly.

Find 6

Capybaras
Related to the guinea pig, the capybara is the largest rodent in the world.

Find 7

Spider monkeys
Spider monkeys can use their long tail, like another arm, for gripping.

Find 7

Bird-eating spiders
These large tarantulas hardly ever eat birds. They prefer snakes and lizards.

Find 1

Jaguar
The rare, spotted jaguar is South America's biggest cat.

Find 7

Macaws
This bright parrot has a large beak and a long tail.

Find 11

Golden lion tamarins
These small monkeys have orange hair around their heads, like lions' manes.

 **Find 5**

Toucans
Toucans use their large, hollow beaks to pluck and peel fruit.

Find 4 **Tapirs**
Tapirs feed on leaves and shoots, and are excellent swimmers.

Find 9  **Poison-dart frogs**
The poison on this frog's skin was once used on arrow tips.

THE HIGH ANDES

The Andes are the longest chain of mountains in the world. Most animals here have thick fur to keep them warm.

Find 5

Condors
These vultures are the largest flying birds in the world.

Find 5

Llamas
Llamas are South American camels that have been trained to carry loads for farmers.

Find 5

Guanacos
When threatened, the guanaco will often spit.

Find 9

Flamingos
Flamingos scoop up water with their bills to eat the tiny plants it contains.

Find 8

Guinea pigs
This rodent keeps its own nest but shares tunnels with other guinea pigs.

Find 1

Spectacled bear
South America's only native bear eats mostly plants and fruit.

Find 11

Chinchillas
Chinchillas are soft-furred rodents that live under rocks and in burrows.

Find 5

Mountain cats
Small, wild mountain cats live on the rocky slopes and hunt rodents.

Find 8

Pumas
These large hunting cats can live in high mountains, jungle, or desert.

Find 6

Huemals
The stocky south Andean deer is built for climbing over the rocky ground.

WOODLAND WONDERS

In this European woodland, the trees lose their leaves in winter. Food can be scarce, so animals stock up in the warm months.

Find 5

Red foxes
The sly fox hunts small mammals, then carries them to a quiet spot to eat.

Find 13

Squirrels
Squirrels can race up and down trees with ease.

Find 10

Tawny owls
Tawny owls raise young in a hole in an old tree.

Find 6

Jays
Jays bury acorns to eat over the winter.

Find 9

Hedgehogs
Spiny hedgehogs sniff the ground to find worms and insects.

Find 4

European badgers
Badgers live as families in burrows called setts.

Find 9

Fallow deer
Male deer, called bucks, lock antlers to compete for females.

Find 3

Stoats
In winter, northern stoats turn all white and are then called ermine.

Find 5

Weasels
These small predators will chase their prey up trees and into burrows.

Find 4

Green woodpeckers
The woodpecker uses its long, sticky tongue to slurp up ants.

79

THE HEAT IS ON

Animals that live in the desert need to survive in great heat and cold, and to manage without water for long periods of time.

Find 3

Camels
One-humped camels can go for weeks without water.

Find 6

Spotted hyenas
These meat-eaters are also known as laughing hyenas, for their whooping calls.

Find 3

Fennec foxes
This small, large-eared fox has furry feet for walking on hot sand.

Find 5

Oryxes
To save water, this antelope only sweats when its body is very hot.

Find 8

Ostriches
The ostrich is the largest living bird. It lays eggs 24 times the size of hens' eggs.

80

Addaxes
These rare antelopes have white coats in summer. These coats reflect the hot sun.

Find 7

Deathstalker scorpions
The sting from the tail of this scorpion is very painful.

Find 3

Monitor lizards
Large monitor lizards hibernate for half the year.

Find 13

Dung beetles
Dung beetles roll animal dung away to use as food.

Find 5

Jerboas
The fast-hopping jerboa is active at night, feeding on seeds and leaves.

MOUNTAIN REFUGE

In the high, rainy mountains of central Africa, large families of apes feed on the jungle's fresh fruit and leaves.

Find 8

Mountain gorillas

The world's largest apes live as a family with a male silverback in charge.

Find 3

Tree hyraxes

These small mammals feed mostly at night and sleep in tree holes.

Find 8

Chimpanzees

Smart chimpanzees are our closest animal relative.

Find 15

Barbets

Pairs of barbets like to sing to each other in the forest.

Find 9

Duikers

These small and shy antelopes will eat the fruit that monkeys drop on the ground.

Find 8

Double-collared sunbirds
This sunbird uses its long beak to sip nectar from flowers.

Find 11

Weaverbirds
These yellow birds weave hanging nests made from grass and stalks.

Find 6

Golden monkeys
Golden-backed monkeys feed on fruit and bamboo.

Find 4

Turacos
When it is scared, this crested bird makes a noisy alarm call.

Find 3

Forest elephants
This elephant has tusks that point downward to help it move through the jungle.

Find 5

Civets

Civets are night-time hunters. They eat insects and steals birds' eggs.

Find 11

Malagasy giant rats

These large rodents can jump very high into the air.

Find 7

Giant chameleons

A chameleon's tongue is longer than its body. It uses it to catch insects.

AFTER DARK

In the Madagascan jungle, night is the time for hunters to come out. Their large eyes and sensitive ears help them find food in the dark.

Find 9

Flying foxes

Flying foxes are large bats that bite fruit to squeeze out the juice.

Find 4

Mouse lemurs

The mouse lemur is the world's smallest primate.

Find **5**

Aye-ayes
The aye-aye has a long middle finger for plucking grubs from under tree bark.

Find **8**

Geckos
Geckos catch flies. They have sticky feet for climbing up trees.

Find **6**

Streaked tenrecs
This spiny worm-eater looks like a mixture of a shrew and a hedgehog.

Find **2**

Fossas
The fossa often climbs trees to catch its main prey, the lemur.

Find **3**

Madagascar long-eared owls
These night hunters catch rats and small lemurs.

SOLUTIONS

4–5 BEACH BEASTS

- Mastodonsaurus
- Tanystropheus
- Liliensternus
- Plateosaurus
- Gerrothorax
- Thecodontosaurus
- Procompsognathus
- Ruehleia
- Saltopus
- Placochelys

6–7 GRAZING GIANTS

- Brachiosaurus
- Hesperosaurus
- Apatosaurus
- Dryosaurus
- Allosaurus
- Diplodocus
- Camptosaurus
- Stegosaurus
- Gargoyleosaurus
- Camarasaurus

8–9 FLYING HIGH

- Gnathosaurus
- Pterodactylus
- Anurognathus
- Dakosaurus
- Aerodactylus
- Libellulium
- Archaeopteryx
- Dimorphodon
- Rhamphorhynchus
- Scaphognathus

10–11 STAMPEDE!

- Pachyrhinosaurus
- Centrosaurus
- Corythosaurus
- Atrociraptor
- Prosaurolophus
- Albertosaurus
- Euoplocephalus
- Lambeosaurus
- Pachycephalosaurus
- Edmontonia

SOLUTIONS

12–13 FLOODLAND FEAST

- Eotyrannus
- Hylaeosaurus
- Pelorosaurus
- Baryonyx
- Hypsilophodon
- Polacanthus
- Valdosaurus
- Neovenator
- Iguanodon
- Becklespinax

14–15 SAVAGE SEAS

- Hybodus
- Xiphactinus
- Ichthyosaur
- Elasmosaurus
- Kronosaurus
- Nautilus
- Ammonite
- Mosasaurus
- Protosphyraena
- Archelon

16–17 SWAMP DWELLERS

- Champsosaurus
- Thescelosaurus
- Albertosaurus
- Adocus
- Puertasaurus
- Ankylosaurus
- Anzu
- Edmontosaurus
- Pteranodon
- Triceratops

18–19 T. REX TUSSLE

- Tyrannosaurus rex
- Ornithomimus
- Dryptosaurus
- Thescelosaurus
- Alamosaurus
- Dracorex
- Saurolophus
- Ojoraptorsaurus
- Leptoceratops
- Gorgosaurus

SOLUTIONS

20–21 BABY BITERS

- Troodon
- Troodon young
- Parasaurolophus
- Dragonflies
- Edmontosaurus
- Triceratops
- Helopanoplia
- Hadrosaurus
- Brachychamsa
- Panoplosaurus

22–23 ON THE HUNT

- Velociraptor
- Gallimimus
- Harpymimus
- Protoceratops
- Altirhinus
- Adasaurus
- Talarurus
- Avimimus
- Bactrosaurus
- Garudimimus

24–25 BUSY BARN

- Horses
- Ponies
- Donkeys
- Llamas
- Barn owls and owlets
- Saddles
- Rats
- Mice
- Chickens
- Swallows

26–27 POND SPLASHING

- Ducks
- Moorhens
- Frogs
- Dragonflies
- Nests
- Grey heron
- Tadpoles
- Geese
- Coots
- Toads

SOLUTIONS

28–29 COUNTING SHEEP

- Shepherd
- Sheepdogs
- Ewes
- Black sheep
- Feeding troughs
- Crows
- Lambs
- Young ewes
- Rabbits
- Rams

30–31 BEST IN SHOW

- Prize cups
- Horses
- Rosettes
- Tractors
- Bulls
- Carriages
- Horseboxes
- Foals
- Sheep
- Pigs

32–33 MACHINES IN ACTION

- Tractors
- Spreaders
- Four-wheel drive cars
- Seed drills
- Cats
- Cultivators
- Bales
- Harrows
- Wheelbarrows
- Round baler

34–35 COSY FARMHOUSE

- Fried eggs
- Sausages
- Cheeses
- Butter
- Bottles of milk
- Sweater
- Vegetables
- Fruit preserves
- Slices of bread
- Pears

SOLUTIONS

36—37 URBAN FARM

- Guinea pigs
- Rabbits
- Goats
- Piglets
- Lambs
- Piles of straw
- Ducks
- Chickens
- Ice creams
- Milk bottles

38—39 FLYING FRIENDS

- Rooster
- Turkeys
- Quails
- Eggs
- Guinea fowls
- Fox
- Chicken food
- Poultry feeders
- Sparrows
- Hen

40—41 ROUNDUP!

- Windmills
- Cattle
- Calves
- Cowgirls and cowboys
- Lassos
- Ranch houses
- Rattlesnakes
- Coyotes
- Cowboy hats
- Horses

42—43 BABY ANIMALS

- Ducklings
- Piglets
- Kittens
- Goslings
- Lambs
- Calves
- Foals
- Cygnets
- Chicks
- Kids

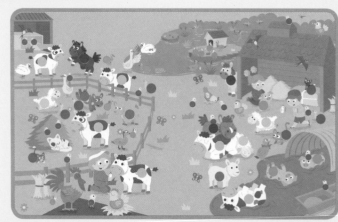

SOLUTIONS

44–45 OVER THE REEF

- Clownfish
- Angelfish
- Sweetlips
- Picasso triggerfish
- Bird wrasses
- Parrotfish
- Soldierfish
- Masked pufferfish
- Napoloeon wrasses
- Butterflyfish

46–47 CHILLY NORTH

- Polar bears
- Arctic chars
- Ribbon seals
- Narwhals
- Beluga whales
- Bowhead whale
- Ringed seals
- Guillemots
- Arctic cod
- Walruses

48–49 DARK DEPTHS

- Anglerfish
- Pelican eels
- Deep-sea jellyfish
- Hagfish
- Giant oarfish
- Viperfish
- Lanternfish
- Vampire squid
- Fangtooth
- Black swallowers

50–51 ROCKY SHORE

- Sea stars
- Hermit crabs
- Common octopuses
- Cormorants
- Sea scorpions
- Common blennies
- Sea urchins
- Moon jellyfish
- Common seals
- Mussels

SOLUTIONS

52–53 ANCIENT SHIPWRECK

- Lionfish
- Redcoat squirrelfish
- Scuba divers
- Spadefish
- Bluestripe snappers
- Bluefin trevallies
- Coral groupers
- Bannerfish
- Devil scorpionfish
- Moray eels

54–55 KELP FOREST

- Mako sharks
- John dory
- Marblefish
- Stingrays
- Red pigfish
- Yellowtail kingfish
- Spotted black groupers
- Blue maomaos
- Common triplefins
- Porcupine fish

56–57 MANGROVE MAZE

- Saltwater crocodiles
- Yellow sea horses
- Mud crabs
- Anchovies
- Mudskippers
- Mullets
- Combtooth blennies
- Cardinalfish
- Mangrove jacks
- Banded archerfish

58–59 SUNKEN CITY

- Zebra sea breams
- White-spotted octopuses
- Dogfish
- Cornetfish
- Eagle rays
- Stargazers
- Sea potatoes
- Sea hares
- Red sea stars
- Bearded fireworms

SOLUTIONS

60–61 NIGHT DIVE

- Cleaner shrimp
- Decorator crabs
- Sea kraits
- Polyps
- Epaulette sharks
- Blackspotted puffers
- Pineapple sea cucumbers
- Slipper lobsters
- Crown-of-thorns starfish
- Cuttlefish

62–63 SANDY SEA BED

- Clams
- Lobsters
- Skates
- Horseshoe crabs
- Haddocks
- Oyster toadfish
- Herrings
- Red gurnards
- Scallops
- Flounders

64–65 SUPER SAFARI

- African elephants
- Lions
- Wildebeest
- Cheetahs
- Baboons
- Crocodiles
- Zebras
- Giraffes
- Black rhinos
- Impalas

66–67 FROZEN FIELDS

- Muskoxen
- Arctic hares
- Wolves
- Arctic foxes
- Reindeer
- Polar bears
- Walruses
- Lemmings
- Snow geese
- Snowy owls

SOLUTIONS

68–69 PINE FOREST

- Lynx
- Snowshoe hares
- Wolverines
- Black bears
- Beavers
- Muskrats
- Porcupines
- Pine martens
- Moose
- White-tailed deer

70–71 GRASSLAND GRAZERS

- Bison
- Golden eagles
- Black-footed ferrets
- Burrowing owls
- Jackrabbits
- American badgers
- Prairie dogs
- Pronghorns
- Coyotes
- Rattlesnakes

72–73 INCREDIBLE ISLANDS

- Green sea turtles
- Marine iguanas
- Flightless cormorants
- Frigate birds
- Humpback whales
- Blue-footed boobies
- Fur seals
- Sea lions
- Giant tortoises
- Lava lizards

74–75 AMAZON ACTIVITIES

- Sloths
- Capybaras
- Spider monkeys
- Bird-eating spiders
- Jaguar
- Tapirs
- Poison-dart frogs
- Toucans
- Golden lion tamarins
- Macaws

SOLUTIONS

76–77 THE HIGH ANDES

- Condors
- Llamas
- Guanacos
- Flamingos
- Guinea pigs
- Pumas
- Huemals
- Mountain cats
- Chinchillas
- Spectacled bear

78–79 WOODLAND WONDERS

- Red foxes
- Squirrels
- Tawny owls
- Jays
- Hedgehogs
- Weasels
- Green woodpeckers
- Stoats
- Fallow deer
- European badgers

80–81 THE HEAT IS ON

- Camels
- Spotted hyenas
- Fennec foxes
- Oryxes
- Ostriches
- Dung beetles
- Jerboas
- Monitor lizards
- Deathstalker scorpions
- Addaxes

82–83 MOUNTAIN REFUGE

- Mountain gorillas
- Tree hyraxes
- Chimpanzees
- Barbets
- Duikers
- Turacos
- Forest elephants
- Golden monkeys
- Weaverbirds
- Double-collared sunbirds

26–27 AFTER DARK

- Civets
- Malagasy giant rats
- Giant chameleons
- Flying foxes
- Mouse lemurs
- Fossas
- Madagascar long-eared owls
- Streaked tenrecs
- Geckos
- Aye-ayes

FUN SPOTS

Now go back through the book
to see if you can find these cute characters!